D1209827

Fun in American Folk Rhymes

FUN
☆ IN ☆
AMERICAN
FOLK RHYMES

By Ray Wood

WITH DRAWINGS BY
ED HARGIS

AND AN INTRODUCTION BY
CARL CARMER

J. B. Lippincott Company
PHILADELPHIA AND NEW YORK

INTRODUCTION
BY CARL CARMER

When men began to find out that words, and even sounds, can be strung together in groups and uttered, one after the other, in a way that delights the ear, the first folk verses were born. Ever since that time people have been charmed by such bits and snatches of word-music and have passed them on to their children and grandchildren.

Some of these prize-packages filled with entrancing words or syllables have stuck in our memories because of their catchy rhythms, some because of their pleasing repetitions of similar sounds, which we call rhymes. Some have charmed us because they say something wise or clever or funny. Others make no sense at all and we love them for being so ridiculous, for saying nothing at all with liveliness and humor.

Folk rhymes for the most part are short because they are not usually to be found on printed pages but must depend on the memories of men for living on. One may come from an old song and be all that is left of it because the rest of its words have long been forgotten. Another may have been made up by boys and girls who have wanted to have rhythmic verses to repeat while they were playing active games. That is how skip-rope rhymes began, and rhymes to be said to the rhythms of bouncing balls, and counting out rhymes, like "eenie, meenie, minie mo," which will finally tell who is going to be "it." Many of our folk rhymes have been built out of the daily lives we live and the jobs we do, and they come from all over our great country.

You will find in this book that Ray Wood has selected rhymes from the many that have grown out of the usual activities of American hunters, fishers, cowboys, farmers, cooks, and housewives. You will find that they were born in such places as lumber-camps, ranch corrals, barn-yards, city sidewalks, and country kitchens. In his introduction to Mr. Wood's delightful first collection of folk rhymes, *The American Mother Goose,* the late John Lomax, who lived nearly all of his life in the American West and became a great authority on its folk songs, told of Texas evenings when as a child he played such folk games as "one-eyed cat," "town ball," "stink base," and "roley-boley." Children's games vary so much over the wide expanse of America that I, who lived my childhood in a maple-shaded little town in "up-state" New York, recognized only one of these and we called it "one *old* cat" instead of "one-eyed." I recall the names of other games, however,–"duck on a rock," "pom-pom-pullaway," "ten-step," and some of the folk rhymes that went with them.

The most likeable of folk rhymes are frequently the oldest, because countless people of our past have been so pleased with them as the years rolled on that they have kept them alive. Some of them tell us something of the lives of our fathers and our grandfathers and ancestors who lived before them, and we treasure them because they tell us what life was like when America was a young and growing country. A few were born so long ago that they were being said in older countries long before the United States became a nation, and some of this group were brought across the seas from many foreign lands which have given us people who became American citizens. Of course some of these had to be translated from foreign languages into our own and then re-worked into verses that end in English rhymes.

New rhymes are always springing up in America and from much the same kind of beginnings as the old ones. Today or tomorrow you may hear one, and, if it pleases you, it will stick in your memory and you may tell it to your friends. If they like it and remember it too, it may be on its way to being a folk rhyme and may some day be published in a collection like this one.

From his vast knowledge of American folk rhymes Ray Wood has presented us in this book with many colorful and exciting selections. American readers should be very grateful to him for this stimulating labor-of-love. Many a grown-up will read all of these rhymes for the happy days they will recall. Many a teacher will recommend them to classes of children, not only to awaken in them a sense of the rhythm of words—which is the beginning of an understanding and appreciation of all poetry—but also to provide them with a knowledge of this land of ours and its people. Many a child will read them for the sheer joy they will bring to his senses, his mind, and his heart.

CONTENTS

CONTENTS

CONTENTS

CONTENTS

AUTHOR'S FOREWORD

The earliest child rhymes we know are the Mother Goose rhymes and some of these were known so long ago that one may only guess when they were first used. Many of these, perhaps most of them, were made up by older folk, but because they were funny, or had the charm of rhyme or fantasy, they were appropriated by the children, who told them to each other, and remembered them when they grew up and repeated them to their children until, when they were finally published in books, they were thought of only as child rhymes.

When the colonists came to this country from England they brought, among their memories, some of these rhymes, but their children, and their children's children, growing up in surroundings far different from those of the old world, invented new games, and new rhymes to sing or chant as they played them; they found new objects and animals about which to make rhymes and new circumstances of living which were interesting enough to call for rhymes.

As the population spread over the land, children who lived in the country might chant about 'possums or raccoons, or perhaps jaybirds, hoot owls or woodpeckers—which to some of them seemed more interesting as "peckerwoods." In the South children might rhyme about bullfrogs or alligators. In the plains country they might ask, "What kind of pants does a cowboy wear?" In the cities they might chant, " 'Fire! Fire!' shouted Mrs. McGuire," or "Help! Murder! Police!" and, because a railroad locomotive is a thing of wonder and glory to all children, all of them would chant the praises of "Engine, Engine, Number Nine."

Only a few of the hundreds of rhymes used by American children are included in this book; some of them are here published for the first time. The authorship of a few is well known, but for the most part it would be very difficult to tell where they came from or who invented them.

Some were undoubtedly made up by the children themselves, others by older folk, but because children claimed them as their own, they have been kept alive by children, when otherwise they might have been long forgotten.

"Bye, Baby Bunting," is probably the oldest and best known of all American nursery rhymes. It would probably be impossible to determine when or where it came into use or who invented it. "This little pig says, 'I'm going to steal some corn,' " used to count the baby's toes, was doubtless inspired by the Mother Goose rhyme, "This little pig went to market." Likewise, the rhyme "I had a little horse; his name was Dapple-gray," which is used to play a "ride-a-cock-horse" game with young children, may have been inspired by a similar rhyme in the classic Mother Goose.

"East side, West side, All around the town," is the chorus of a song titled, "The Sidewalks of New York," so popular from the time of its introduction about sixty-five years ago, that it immediately became part of the lore of the children of that city and probably will remain so as long as the city of New York exists. It was written by Charles V. Lawlor and James W. Blake.

"Me, and my wife and a bob-tailed dog," was an additional verse to the song "Little Brown Jug," sung in an early minstrel show. Children seem to have preferred it over other verses of the song.

Early minstrel shows very often included well-known folk rhymes in their acts, and, because such acts were very popular, the performers sometimes made up rhymes or songs, which were so well liked by children that when they grew up they taught them to their own children.

"Brian O'Lin" may have originated in the old country, but the version included in this book is, for the most part, American invention, and a song very similar to this version was sung as a regular act in several well-known minstrel shows.

"The Monkey's Wedding" was very likely made up by minstrel performers, for it was a popular minstrel song. However, the first four verses have been preserved as child rhymes for many years.

The song, "Springfield Mountain" was a serious poem written about 1761. Quite likely the melody associated with it, a twangy tune very much like the music of a jews-harp, caused it to develop into a humorous song and to become a favorite of American children.

The "old soldier who had a wooden leg" seems to have been composed about the time of the Civil War, and has been a childhood favorite since.

"I had a little sweetheart no bigger than my thumb" is the American version of a rhyme of the classic Mother Goose, "I had a little husband no bigger than my thumb," which is said to have been sung in ridicule of King Philip of Spain when he married Mary Tudor, Queen of England.

"There was an old bachelor who lived all alone" and "Hickety-pickety, my black hen" are also variations of classic Mother Goose rhymes.

Fun in American Folk Rhymes

When I was a little boy I had no sense;
I bought me a fiddle for fifteen cents.
All the tunes that I could play
Were Yankee Doodle and Nix-ver-stay.

Fuzzy-wuzzy was a bear;
Fuzzy-wuzzy cut his hair;
Then Fuzzy-wuzzy wasn't fuzzy, was he?

East Side, West Side, all around the town,
The kids played ring-a-rosy, London Bridge is
    falling down.
Boy and girl together, me and Mamie O'Rourke,
Tripping the light fantastic on the sidewalks of
    New York.

Fodder in the barn loft,
Poultry in the yard;
Meat in the smokehouse;
Barrel full of lard;
Milk in the dairy;
Butter on the board;
Coffee in a little bag,
And sugar in the gourd.
You roll the gourd about
To get the sugar out.

I had a little pup, his name was Spot
Whenever we cooked, he licked the pot,
Every time we ate, he never forgot,
And he licked the dishes as well as the pot.

I went to the river and couldn't get across,
I jumped on an alligator—thought it was a horse.
I spurred him with my heels and he began to roar.
I nearly burnt the water up a-gettin' to the shore.

———

Little Tee Wee
Went to sea
In a little boat
And while afloat
The little boat bended
And now the story's ended.

———

Chicken in the car and the car won't go,
That's the way to spell C-H-I-C-A-G-O!

Knife and a fork and a bottle and a cork,
That's the way to spell N-E-W-- Y-O-R-K.

9

One for the cut worm,
Two for the crow,
Three for the chickens,
And four to grow.

I had a little pig, I fed him in a trough,
But he got so fat that his tail dropped off.
So I got me a hammer and I got me a nail,
And I made my little pig a brand new tail.

One night I heard my old dog bark,
   I thought he'd treed a coon,
But when I got outside I found
   He was barking at the moon.

Come on Smarty, guess my riddle;
Poor Miles has it right in the middle;
Luke has it first, Paul has it last;
Girls have it once and boys never have it.
Neither you nor I have it, or ever expect
        to,
But Willie has it twice and so does Millie.
Doctor Lowell has it in front and behind
        at the same time
And twice as bad behind as in front.
Bridget Sullivan had it twice in the same
        place
Until she married Paddy McGinty
And now she hasn't got it any more.

———————

One, two, three, four,
Mama scrubbed the kitchen floor,
Floor dried, baby cried.
One, two, three, four.

The fly made a visit to the grocery store
Didn't even knock—went right in the door.
He took a bite of sugar, and took a bite of ham,
Then sat down to rest on the grocery man.

———

If I ever marry,
I'll marry a fisherman's daughter,
Then my wife can row the boat
And the children can play in the water.

———

My mammy had a speckled hen,
    She was faithful, tried and true.
Every day she laid an egg,
    On Sunday, she laid two.

Someone scared our speckled hen,
    I wish they'd let her be;
Every day she laid two eggs,
    On Sunday she laid three.

Now this old speckled hen of ours,
    She laid behind the door;
Every day she laid three eggs,
    On Sunday she laid four.

But now our speckled hen is gone,
    I wish she was alive;
Every day she laid four eggs,
    On Sunday she laid five.

Pollywog on a log
Wiggly-wagged his tail.
Bumblebee saw a flea
Sitting on a rail.

Grasshopper eating supper
With a butterfly;
Ladybug on a rug
Heard the cricket cry.

Katydid ran and hid
In a maple tree.
Miller-mollar stole a dollar
From a chickadee.

Yellow jacket with a racket
Made the hornet run.
Dragonfly hurt his eye
Looking at the sun.

The funniest sight I've ever seen
Was a bullfrog sewing on a sewing machine.
He sewed so fast and fine and wide
He sewed a polecat's tail to a tomcat's hide.

Spinning Jenny and Hoppin' John
Crawled in bed with their gaiters on;
One shoe on and one shoe off,
And both of them caught the whooping cough.

———————

"Jaybird pulls the turnin' plow
    Sparrow, why not you?"
"My legs' so long and spindlin'
    I'm 'fraid they'll break in two."

———————

Go tell Aunt Rhoda,
Go tell Aunt Rhoda,
Go tell Aunt Rhoda,
   Her gray goose is dead.

The one she was saving,
The one she was saving,
The one she was saving,
   To make a feather bed.

She died this morning,
She died this morning,
She died this morning,
   Just at break of day.

When we go tell her,
When we go tell her,
When we go tell her,
   What will Auntie say?

Aunt Rhoda's grieving,
Aunt Rhoda's grieving,
Aunt Rhoda's grieving,
    Because her goose is dead.

For she was planning,
For she was planning,
For she was planning,
    To make a feather bed.

Fireman, Fireman Number Eight,
Struck his head against the gate.
The gate flew in, the gate flew out
And that's the way the fire went out.

Pass one window, ty-de-o.
Pass two windows, ty-de-o,
Pass three windows, ty-de-o.
Jingle at the windows, ty-de-o!

Ty-de-o, ty-de-o.
Jingle at the windows, ty-de-o!

Pass one station, ty-de-o,
Pass two stations, ty-de-o,
Pass three stations, ty-de-o,
Whistle for the crossing, ty-de-o.

Pass one red light, ty-de-o,
Pass two red lights, ty-de-o,
Pass three red lights, ty-de-o,
Fine ten dollars, ty-de-o.

Peckerwood pecking on the old church steeple,
When he pecks it down, it will fall on the people.
Go peck on the schoolhouse or peck on a tree;
Peck on anything, but don't peck on me.

It ain't gonna rain no more,
It ain't gonna rain no more;
How in heck can I wash my neck
If it ain't gonna rain no more?

———

Jaybird settin' on a barbed-wire fence,
Tryin' to make a dollar out of fifteen cents.

———

THE OLD SOW TOOK THE MEASLES

The old sow took the measles and died in the
spring.
What'll we do with the old sow's head?
Make as good an oven as ever baked bread.

Oven or skillet, or any such a thing;
The old sow took the measles and died in the
  spring.

What'll we do with the old sow's ears?
Make as good a snare drum as ever you did
  hear.
Snare drum or tambourine or any such a thing;
The old sow took the measles and died in the
  spring.

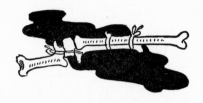

What'll we do with the old sow's bones?
Make as good a shotgun as anybody owns.
Shotgun or rifle or any such a thing;
The old sow took the measles and died in the
     spring.

What'll we do with the old sow's teeth?
Make as good needles as ever sewed cloth.
Needles or pins or any such a thing;
The old sow took the measles and died in the
     spring.

What'll we do with the old sow's nose?
Make as good a fox horn as anybody blows.
Fox horn or cowbell or any such a thing;
The old sow took the measles and died in the
    spring.

What'll we do with the old sow's hair?
Make as good britches as a body'd want to
    wear.
Britches or jacket or any such a thing;
The old sow took the measles and died in the
    spring.

What'll we do with the old sow's feet?
Make as good knife handle as you ever took
   to meat.
Knife handle, spoon handle, any such a thing;
The old sow took the measles and died in the
   spring.

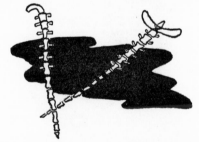

What'll we do with the old sow's spine?
Make as good a walkin' stick as ever helped
   the blind.
Walkin' stick or crutch or any such a thing;
The old sow took the measles and died in the
   spring.

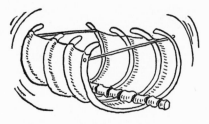

What'll we do with the old sow's ribs?
Make as good a cradle as ever rocked a babe.
Cradle or a high chair or any such a thing;
The old sow took the measles and died in the
    spring.

What'll we do with the old sow's hide?
Make as good a saddle as any preacher rides.
Saddle or bridle or any such a thing;
The old sow took the measles and died in the
    spring.

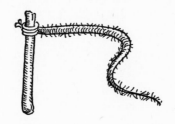

What'll we do with the old sow's tail?
Make as good a whip as ever drove the mail.
Whip or quirt or any such a thing;
The old sow took the measles and died in the
spring.

I went to the river and couldn't get across;
I paid five dollars for an old gray horse;
When I got in the water, the horse couldn't swim;
I paid five dollars to get him out again.

―――――

When Markham Toots blew out the light
   He always blew so hard
He blew it through the window sash
   And out into the yard.

―――――

As I went walking down the road
I met a terrapin and a toad;
The terrapin commenced to sing,
And the toad, he cut the pigeon wing.

I had a little sweetheart no bigger than my thumb,
I put her in a coffeepot battered like a drum,
I took it by the handle and threw it in the river,
Saying: "Goodby, my sweetheart, goodby, my
honey,
If it hadn't been for you I might have had a little
money."

———

Riddledy Bob and Jimson Weed
Fed their wives on hound dog feed;
Wives chased squirrels, dogs laid idle.
I wouldn't have neither for a silver-set bridle.

———

I had a little dog, his name was Tim;
I put him in a bathtub to see could he swim;
He drank all the water and ate all the soap
And almost died with a bubble in his throat.

———

35

Little Jimmy Jimsonweed
Went to take a ride;
His boat turned over
And he fell into the tide.

If all the parents in the world
Would teach their kids to swim,
They wouldn't have to hire a dredge
To find poor little Jim.

Said the monkey to the owl,
"What will you have to drink?"
"Well, since you're so very kind,
I'll take a bottle of ink."

Five little chickadees, sitting in a door;
One flew away and then there were four.
Four little chickadees sitting in a tree;
One flew away and then there were three.
Three little chickadees looking at you;
One flew away and then there were two.
Two little chickadees sitting in the sun;
One flew away and then there was one.
One little chickadee sitting all alone;
He flew away and then there was none.

Mr. Baker, Mr. Baker, the good old shoemaker,
Half-soled his shoes with a piece of brown paper;
When the paper grew thin and the water seeped
    in
What a terrible fix Mr. Baker was in.

This little pig says, "I'm goin' to steal some corn."
This little pig says, "Where are you goin' to get it?"
This little pig says, "Out of the old man's barn."
This little pig says, "I'm goin' to tell on you."
This little pig says, "Wee-wee! I can't get over the doorsill!"

───────────

THE MONKEY'S WEDDING

The monkey married the baboon's sister,
Smacked his lips each time he kissed her,
Kissed so hard he raised a blister,
   She set up a yell.

Bridesmaids stuck on some court plaster,
It stuck so hard it couldn't stick faster,
Surely it was a sad disaster,
   But it soon got well.

What do you think the bride was dressed in?
Cheesecloth veil and green glass breastpin,
Red kid shoes, quite interestin',
   She was quite a belle.

The bridegroom wore a white stiff collar,
Black silk stock that cost a dollar,
White kid gloves the style to follow,
   He was quite a swell.

The Chimpanzee read the wedding service,
Dressed up like a whirling dervish,
The best man stumbled, slightly nervous
   And near forgot the ring.

Surely was a great occasion
Monkeys there of all persuasions,
The wedding march in great elation,
    All began to sing.

What do you think they had for supper?
Ripe bananas fried in butter,
Appetites were all a-flutter,
    Waiting for the call.

Coconuts both boiled and roasted,
Peanuts raw and peanuts toasted,
Music in the corner posted,
  To begin the ball.

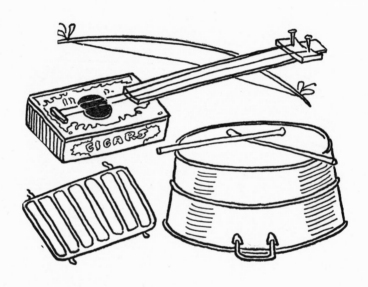

What do you think they had for a fiddle?
A cigar box with a hole in the middle,
A washtub drum and a rusty griddle,
  All struck up a song.

What do you think was the tune they danced to?
"Drunken Sailor"; how they pranced too,
Tails were stepped on when they chanced to
   Be a bit too long.

How they frisked and whirled and chattered,
Lady monks were highly flattered,
When they waltzed–'twas all that mattered,
   Such a grand affair.

All the guests were quite contented,
Everyone was represented,
When best wishes were presented
   To the happy pair.

At the height of their pleasant folly,
When everyone was feeling jolly,
Came the keepers melancholy,
   Everything went wrong.

A sight to serve a man for wages,
Though it was a bit outrageous,
When they took them back to their cages.
 And that's the end of my song.

———————

How much do you love me?
How much do you love me?
A bushel and a peck
And a hug around the neck,
That's how much I love you.

———

Little boy, little boy,
Who made your britches?
Daddy cut them out
And Mammy sewed the stitches.

———

Three little bugs in a basket,
Hardly room for two;
One like Mary, one like Tom
And one that looks like you.

Betty Baker bought some butter,
"But," said she "this butter's bitter,
If I put it in my batter
It will make the batter bitter."
So she bought some better butter,
Butter that was not so bitter,
Put this butter in her batter,
Thus she made the batter better.

━━━━━━

If I was a farmer, I'd have an easy time;
I'd pick the nice red apples from the nice red
apple vine;
I'd pick delicious watermelons from the water-
melon tree,
And oh, how happy I would be!

━━━━━━

Whoo! Whoo! Who cooks for you-all?
Whoo! Whoo! Who cooks for you-all?
 My sister Sue boils the stew,
 Who cooks for you-all?

Bye, Baby Bunting;
Daddy's gone a-hunting,
To get a little rabbit skin
To wrap the Baby Bunting in.

———

I went to see if my old hen
Had hatched her eggs, there should be ten;
She'd hatched them out, but only nine,
And all were sitting on a pumpkin vine.

———

Engine, engine, Number Nine,
Running on Chicago line;
See her sparkle, see her shine,
Engine, engine, Number Nine.

I had a little pig, his name was Ben,
He learned to count from one to ten.
I dressed him up to look like a clerk
With a collar and tie and sent him to work.

———

Old Sam Brodie lost his cow;
He lost his cow and could not find her;
When he had done all he could do
His cow came home with her tail behind her.

———

I had a little mule, her name was Jenny;
When I bought that mule she cost me plenty;
But I sold that mule for one little penny;
And now I have neither the penny nor Jenny.

What will we do with the baby-oh?
When we go down to Jericho?
Wrap him up in calico
And take him to see his daddy-oh.

———

Hushaby, don't you cry,
Go to sleep, little baby.
When you wake you shall have some cake
And go to see your daddy.

———

He-hi, gimme a piece of pie.
If you lost your diamond ring
Would you sing?
Or would you sigh,
Or would you cry?
Or would you gimme a piece of pie?

A little sparrow built his nest, up in a waterspout.
Down came a thunderstorm and washed the
　　sparrow out.
Then came the sunshine and dried up the rain.
And the little sparrow built his nest up in the
　　spout again.

———————

I had a little hen, her name was Blue;
Every time she laid an egg, she laid two;
She laid in the stove, she laid in the flue,
And she laid a dozen eggs in grandpa's shoe.

I had a little horse,
His name was Dapple-gray,
I sent him to the barn,
To get himself some hay.
First he walked,
Then he trotted,
Then he loped,
Then he galloped.

Goodness! Gracious! Have you heard the news?
The geese are going barefoot because they have
    no shoes?
When the cobbler finds his last and when he gets
    some leather
The geese need not go barefoot in all this bitter
    weather.

Baby Bobby in the tub;
Mama forgot to put in the plug;
Oh, what sorrow, oh, what pain;
There goes Bobby down the drain.

———————

BRIAN O'LIN

Brian O'Lin was an Irishman born,
His beard was unshaven, his head was unshorn,
His forehead stuck out and his nose was pushed
    in,
"But I'm not so bad lookin'," said Brian O'Lin.

He lived by himself in a hollow oak tree,
And although all alone, quite contented was he,
The rain would beat hard and the wind would
   blow in;
"They say fresh air is healthy," said Brian O'Lin.

Brian O'Lin, to add to his woes,
Was sadly in need of a new suit of clothes,
Every garment he had was threadbare and thin;
"They'll take more than mending," said Brian
   O'Lin.

Brian O'Lin found he needed some boots,
He cut down a sapling and trimmed off the
   shoots,

The bark he laced up from the sole to the shin;
"They're rough, but they'll wear well," said Brian
    O'Lin.

Brian O'Lin had no breeches to wear,
He took an old sheepskin and made him a pair,

With the skinny side out and the woolly side in;
"Snug pair of breeches," said Brian O'Lin.

Brian O'Lin had no coat to put on,
They took an old goat skin and soon made him
   one,

The horns stuck out right under his chin;
"They'll think it's me whiskers," said Brian
  O'Lin.

Brian O'Lin found he needed a hat,
He soon fashioned one from the hide of a cat,

He fastened it up with a thorn for a pin;
"All I need is a feather," said Brian O'Lin.

Brian O'Lin had no watch to wear,
He pulled up a turnip and scraped it out fair,
He then caught a cricket and tucked it within;
"They'll think it's a tickin'," said Brian O'Lin.

Brian O'Lin found a flea-bitten mare,
Her shoulders were sore and her four feet were
     bare,
She was very discouraged, slab-sided and thin;
"She could do with some fodder," said Brian
     O'Lin.

Brian now needed a saddle to ride,
He made one with the skin of a calf that had died,

The stirrups he fashioned with old bits of tin;
"It's not fine, but it's rugged," said Brian O'Lin.

He lacked now a bridle for guiding his steed,
With cord made from marsh grass he soon filled
    this need,
He fitted it neatly from fetlock to chin;
"I'm ready to ride, now," said Brian O'Lin.

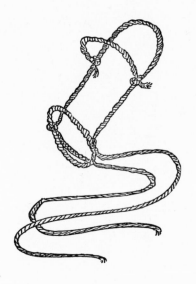

Brian O'Lin a-courtin' would go,
To a widow who lived with her daughter below,
"You're welcome, my lad, we bid you come in!"
"I've come here a-courtin'," said Brian O'Lin.

"We bid you thrice welcome," the poor widow
  said,
"We're desp'rate alone since my husband's been
  dead.

Ye never can know what a mis'ry it's been."
"I want only your daughter," said Brian O'Lin.

"But would you take the child away from her
    mother?
Since she's been a wee bairn, she's never known
    other.
'Tis only we two that are left of the kin."
"Then I'll take the both of ye," said Brian O'Lin.

Brian O'Lin thought to bring his wife home.
He had but one horse, which was all skin and
    bone,
His wife on the pillion as neat as a pin;
"Yer mother before me," said Brian O'Lin.

Brian O'Lin, his wife and her mother,
Were all riding over the bridge together.
The bridge broke down and they all tumbled in;
"There'll be ground at the bottom," said Brian
    O'Lin.

Poor little fly upon the wall,
Ain't you got no clothes at all?
Ain't you got no shimmy-shirt?
Ain't you got no pettiskirt?
Boo!   It's cold!

The raccoon's tail has rings all round,
The possum's tail is bare.
The rabbit has no tail at all,
Just a little bunch of hair.

Every time I come to town,
Folks all kick my dog around;
It makes no difference if he is a hound,
They gotta quit kickin' my dog around.

The boy stood on the burning deck
Eating peanuts by the peck.
His mother called, he would not go,
Because he loved those peanuts so.

———————

Where, oh, where is my little dog gone?
Where, oh, where can he be?
With his ears cut short and his tail cut long,
Oh, where, oh, where can he be?

———————

When I was a little boy, I thought I was a
  bold one,
Daddy bought a new shirt and gave me his
  old one.

Ladies and gentlemen, I'll tell you a fact;
I lost my money in a buffalo track.
The track was large, my money was small;
I hope my speech will please you all.

———————

Joe, Joe, strong and able,
Take your elbows off the table,
You're not living in a stable.

———————

Onezall, twozall, zitterzall, zee,
Striddleum, straddleum, chicken's knee,
Ham, slam, musty jam,
Stringum, strangum, bumble bee;
Stung Jacob on the knee,
Stung his donkey on the snout;
One, two, three, and you're OUT.

Geography, geography is such a pleasant study;
It tells us why the ocean's dry and why the desert's
    muddy.
I study it each morning, each afternoon and then,
I keep the teacher in so I can study it again.

Back in the year of 'fifty-nine,
A guitar grew on a pumpkin vine;
When it got ripe and fell on the ground
A million little banjos grew all around.

One white foot, buy him;
Two white feet, try him;
Three white feet, put him to a dray;
Four white feet, give him away;
Four white feet and a white nose,
Take off his hide and feed him to the
  crows.

When nose itches
Peachtree switches;
Here comes someone
With a hole in his britches.

———

What shall we do for bacon now,
The butcher killed our sandy sow;
She jumped the fence and broke the rail;
Now there's nothing left but her curly tail.

———

Whistle and hoe;
Sing as you go;
Shorten the row
With the songs you **know**.

I had a little monkey, I sent him to the country,
    And fed him on ginger bread.
Along came a choo-choo and knocked him coo-
        coo,
    And now my little monkey is dead.

————

Hickety-pickety, my black hen,
She lays eggs for the railroad men;
Sometimes one, sometimes two,
Sometimes enough for the whole blame crew.

————

Me and my wife and a bob-tail dog
Went across the river on a hickory log;
When the log turned over, we all got wet,
And I caught a cold and I've got it yet.

There was an old hen and she had a black foot;
She laid her eggs by a mulberry root.
She laid more eggs than any hen on the farm;
Another black foot wouldn't do any harm.

———

Hickamore-hackamore
Down on the kitchen floor.
Poor baby tried 'til his fingers were sore
But couldn't pick hickamore-hackamore
Up from the kitchen floor.

(*A sunbeam.*)

———

Grandma said such a curious thing,
"Boys may whistle but girls must sing.
Whistling girls and crowing hens
Always come to some bad end."

The people who live across the way,
At nineteen-eighteen East Broadway,
   Every night they have a fight
And this is what they say.
   "Icky-bicky-soda cracker,
      Icky-bicky-boo;
   Icky-bicky-soda cracker,
      Out goes you."
                    (*a counting out rhyme*)

Monkey, monkey, bottle of beer;
How many monkeys are there here?
One-two-three, out goes he,
With a dirty rag on his knee.
                    (*a counting out rhyme*)

I had a little cow, I milked her in a gourd,
Every time she kicked me I slapped her with a
    board;
When I wasn't looking, she hit me with her tail
And knocked me over in the milking pail.

Big at both ends and small in the middle;
Digs up dirt and sings like a fiddle.

(*A clay wasp*)

———————

I went to the woods and got it;
I sat me down and looked at it;
The more I looked at it the less I liked it;
But I brought it home because I couldn't help it.

(*A thorn.*)

———————

Grasshopper settin' on a sweet potato vine;
Old turkey gobbler came creepin' up behind;
Snatched him down before he changed his mind;
Smacked his lips, says "Sure is fine."

What kind of pants does a cowboy wear?
Rawhide pants, 'cause they don't tear.

SPRINGFIELD MOUNTAIN

On Springfield mow-wow-wowntain
   Once did dwe-we-well
A fine young ma-wa-wan,
   I knew him we-we-well.

Come a ru-di-ru,
Come a ru-di-ru-di-ray.

One Friday mor-wor-worning
   He did go-wo-wo
Down to the mea-wea-weadow
   For to mo-wo-wow.

He scarce had mo-wo-wowed
   Around the fie-wie-wield
When a pizen sar-war-warpint
   Caught his he-we-weel.

He dropped his scy-wy-wythe
   Upon the grou-wou-wound

And closed his ey-wy-wyes
   And looked arou-wou-wound.

And though in a pa-wa-wanic
   He did ca-wa-wall
This poor young ma-wa-wan
   Alone did fa-wa-wall.

His father ha-wa-wastened
   To his si-wi-wide
To see his so-wo-won
   Before he di-wi-wied.

"Oh pappy, de-we-wear
   Go tell my ga-wa-wal
That I'm goin' to di-wi-wie,
   I know I sha-wa-wall."

"Oh good kind pe-we-weople
   Spread the new-wew-wews,
But here comes Sa-wa-wall
   Without her shoe-woe-woes."

"Oh John, oh Joh-woh-wohn,
  Why did you go-wo-wo
Down in the mea-wea-weadow
  For to mo-wo-wow?"

"Now Sally de-we-wear,
  You surely kno-wo-wow
When grass gets ri-wi-wipe
  It must be mo-wo-wowed."

Come all young ga-wa-wals
  And shed a te-we-wear
For a fine young ma-wa-wan
  Who died right he-we-were.

And all young me-we-wen
  A warning ta-wa-wake
And never get bi-wi-wit
  By a rattle-dum-a-sna-wa-wake.

———

There was an old soldier and he had a wooden
    leg,
But he had no tobacco, nor tobacco could he beg.

Another old soldier, as sly as a fox,
Always had tobacco in his old tobacco box.

Said the first old soldier to soldier number two:
"My tobacco box is empty, won't you gimme a
    chew?"

Said the second old soldier: "I'll be dogged if I
    do,
When you no tobacco buy, then you must no to-
    bacco chew."

"If you'd save up your nickels and your pennies
    and your rocks,
You would always have tobacco in your old to-
    bacco box."

Well this first old soldier was feeling pretty mad,
And he says to the other, "I'll get even, my lad."

So he went to the fireplace, took a rifle from its
    peg,
And stabbed the other old soldier with a splinter
    from his leg.

———————

Help! Murder! Police!
My wife fell down in the grease;
I laughed so hard, I fell in the lard.
Help! Murder! Police!

Mabel, Mabel, set the table
Just as fast as you are able;
But next time you must do better
And not forget the salt and pepper!

There was an old bachelor who lived all alone,
He was starved to almost skin and bone;
When he grew tired of such a life
He went to Boston to get a wife.
The roads were muddy, the streets were narrow;
To bring his wife home be bought a wheelbarrow,
But the wheelbarrow broke and down she did fall;
'Twas the last he saw of wheelbarrow, wife and all.

———————

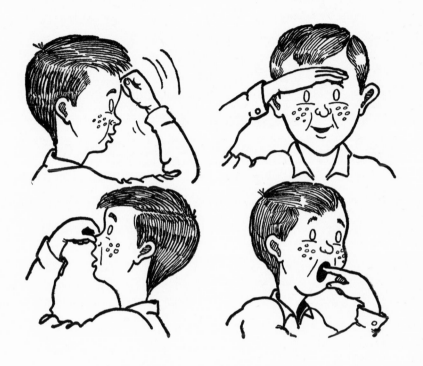

Knock on the door,
Peep in.
Lift the latch
And walk in.

He wears his hat upon his neck
Because he has no head
And he never takes his hat off
Until you're sick in bed.

(*A medicine bottle.*)

As I went up the hazel-dazel
I looked out the razzle-dazzle;
I saw old Mother Middlecum-maddlecum
Tearing up my striddlecum-straddlecum;
If I'd had my diddlecum-daddlecum,
I'd have shot old Mother Middlecum-maddlecum.

I'm a little teapot, short and stout,
Here's my handle, here's my spout,
When I get all steamed up, then I shout
"Tip me up and pour me out!"

I'm wild and woolly and full of fleas,
Ain't never been curried below the knees,
I'm a wild he-wolf from Bitter Creek
And it's my night to howl.

Joe, Joe, broke his toe,
On the way to Mexico;
On the way back he broke his back
Trying to ride a paper sack;
When he got home, he broke a bone
Trying to talk on the telephone.

"Fire!   Fire!"
Cried Mrs. McGuire.
"Where!   Where!"
Cried Mrs. Blair.
"All over town!"
Cried Mrs. Brown.
"Get some water!"
Cried Mrs. Carter.
"We'd better jump!"
Cried Mrs. Gump.
"That would be silly!"
Cried Mrs. Brunelli.
"It looks too risky!"
Cried Mrs. Matruski.
"What'll we do?"
Cried Mrs. LaRue.
"Turn in an alarm!"
Cried Mrs. Storm.
"Save us!   Save us!"
Cried Mrs. Davis.

The fire department got
the call
And the firemen saved
them, one and all.

===============

One, two, three, four, five,
I caught a fish alive.
Six, seven, eight, nine, ten,
I let it go again.

109